A Thick Whisper Of Grace

By

Miriam Arnold

Dedication

This book is dedicated to my best friend, Jacob.

My passion for this message began with you.

Acknowledgement

To the few that read this book in its infancy–

Thank you all for believing in me when I didn't believe in myself. I am certain that this book would still be a file on my computer without your encouragement. Thank you for pestering me.

To the many that are holding this book in their hands–

I hope that this truth changes you as much as it has changed me.

There once lived a man named Moses and he had made some bad choices.

He was ashamed
of what he had done,
so he left his home
and started to run.

When his legs
could run no more,
his body ached
and his feet were sore.

He became a shepherd
and tried to forget
all the mistakes
he'd come to regret.

Moses' plan
was just to stay put.
Little did he know
that Grace was afoot.

"Strange," Moses thought, as he looked at the Bush. "It's been burning for hours, yet it still looks so lush."

Then suddenly, a Voice
sliced the silence in two.
Moses jumped in the air,
no idea what to do.

"Moses!" called the Bush.
The Voice felt like thunder.
It stirred within Moses
both terror and wonder.

"Do not be afraid!
I have big plans for you!"
The Voice felt familiar,
but also quite new.

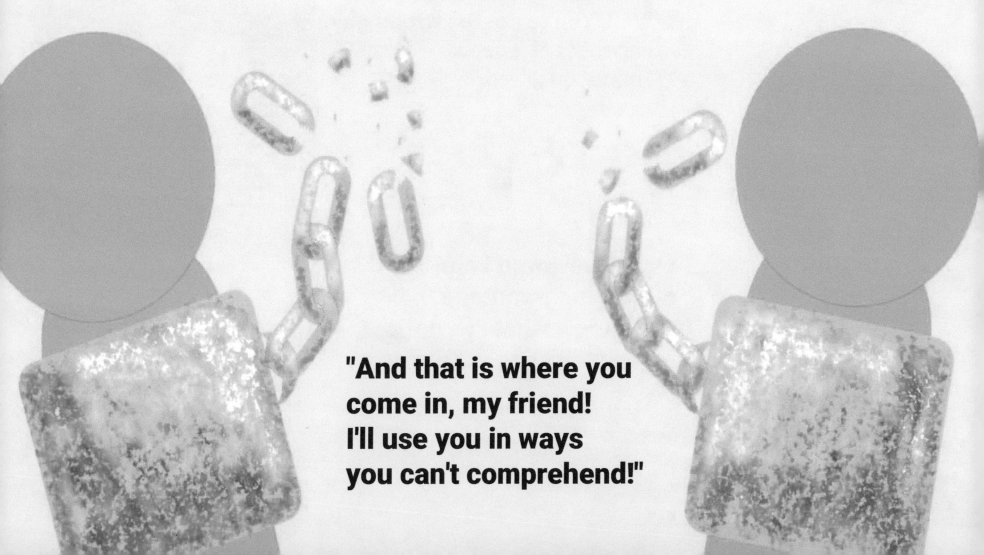

The silence returned
and time seemed to stop.
His face in his hands,
Moses started to sob.

Then light engulfed him,
like a tight, warm embrace.
Yahweh leaned in and breathed
a thick whisper of Grace.

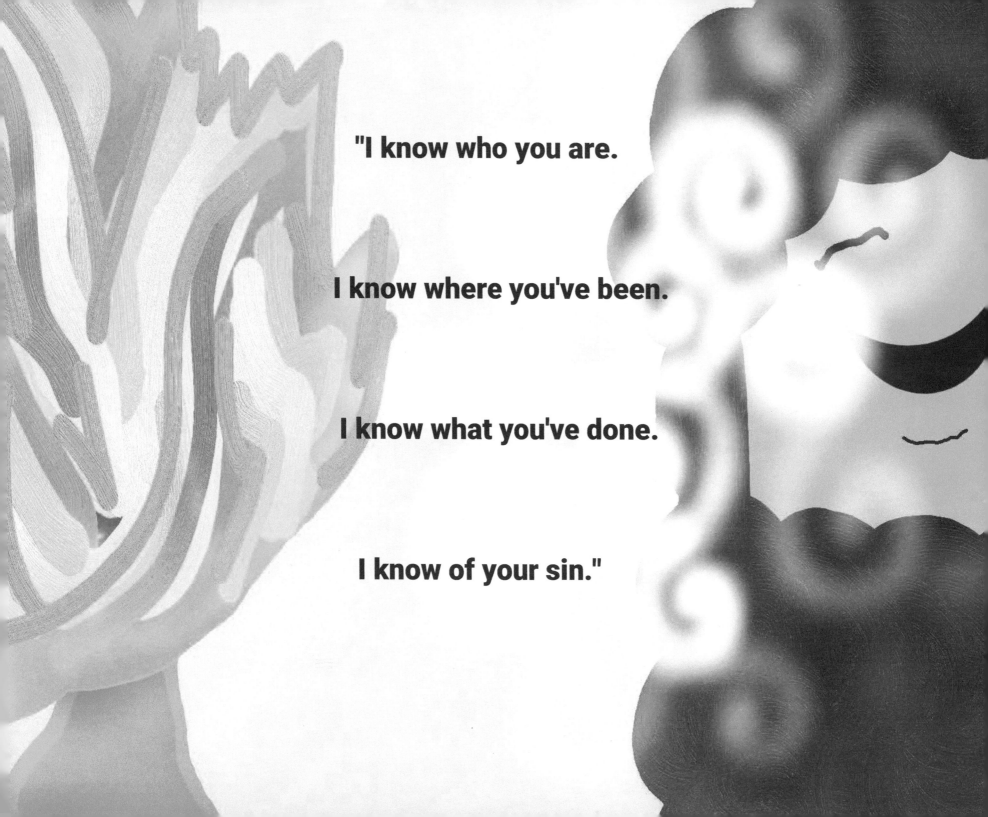

"I know who you are.

I know where you've been.

I know what you've done.

I know of your sin."

"Wake up and see,
it's not about being 'worthy.'
The beauty of Grace is
that you don't deserve it."

And that is why
I've chosen you.
Come now, Moses,
let Me Love you!"

Just as Yahweh promised
deliverance to the slaves,
so, too, did Moses
find Freedom that day.

And from that moment on,
Moses knew who he was.
But not only that,
Moses knew Whose he was.

Some think it strange
that God chooses the Weak.
Some downplay their frailties,
giving their stories a tweak.

God's quite in the business
of using the Broken.
In fact, that is often
just why they were chosen.

Our failures highlight
the true Hero of the Story
It's our need that inevitab
brings Him the Glory.

Discussion Questions

Why did Moses leave his home?

Exodus 2:11-15; Acts 7:23-29

> He did something wrong and was scared that someone would find out.

Have you ever felt that way? What was it like?

How does God feel about us?

Psalm 139; Romans 8:38-39

> He fully knows us and fully loves us.

What does that mean?

Romans 3; Ephesians 2

> His love is unconditional—it does not rely on anything that we do or do not do. If it did, we would never be able to earn it.

How does God's love change the way that we live?
Romans 12:1-2; 1 John 4:7-18

> Knowing God's unconditional love for us makes us brave. It makes us want to show love to Him in return by trusting, seeking and obeying Him.

How does God's love make you feel?

Why did God choose Moses?
Isaiah 42:8; 2 Corinthians 12:9

> God chose him so that no one could look at the Exodus and think that Moses did it on his own. He chose someone who was perfectly imperfect, so that everyone would know that God Himself delivered the Israelites.

What do you think God is going to do through you?

About the Author

Miriam and her husband live in the Greater Atlanta Area with their two daughters. Her favorite thing to do is chat over sugary coffee, but her other hobbies include running, biking, journaling, doodling and playing board games.

CPSIA information can be obtained
at www.ICGtesting.com
Printed in the USA
JSHW040030050623
42651JS00021B/9